WHEN GOD MADE COLOR

BY SHERI CARMON

Dedicated to God's children,
in all of their beautiful colors

Text copyright © 2019 by Sheri Carmon
Artwork copyright © 2019 by Silver Bluebird Studios

WhiteSpark Publishing, a division of WhiteFire Publishing
13607 Bedford Rd NE / Cumberland, MD 21502
www.WhiteSpark-Publishing.com

ISBN: 978-1-946531-16-2 (paperback)
978-1-946531-59-9 (hardcover)
978-1-946531-17-9 (digital)

SILVER
BLUEBIRD
STUDIOS
www.SilverBluebirdStudios.com

Fine prints from this picture book are available at www.SilverBluebirdStudios.com

WHEN GOD MADE
COLOR

STORY BY
Sheri Carmon

PICTURES BY
Silver Bluebird Studios
www.SilverBluebirdStudios.com

WhiteSpark Publishing

The heavens declare the glory of God;
    the skies proclaim the work of his hands.
Day after day they pour forth speech;
    night after night they reveal knowledge.
They have no speech, they use no words;
    no sound is heard from them.
Yet their voice goes out into all the earth,
    their words to the ends of the world...

Psalm 19:1-4   NIV

In the beginning,

the very beginning,
just before the earth was born—

God danced across the waters,
carrying with Him all the colors of the rainbow.
Those colors swirled and foamed,
twirled and mixed, skipped and sang
as He danced through the soft blackness.

God hovered over the waters and said...

"LET THERE

BE LIGHT"

And there was light!
And God called the light "day," and the darkness He called "night."

And God saw that it was good!

At the sound of His voice,

the heavens and the earth separated,
and color streamed through the expanse and raced joyfully across the new sky
in spinning bands of red, orange, yellow, green, blue, indigo, and violet.

Shimmering blue flowed across the wide seas,

and rich brown poured across the land.
Then, God's breath swept green
down upon the earth.

Green grasses emerged, and flowers sprang up with blossoms of every color.

The earth burst forth with life!

And God saw that it was good!

Plants appeared with great green leaves, plentiful seeds, and lush fruit. Deep green forests grew up everywhere with towering trees that reached into the sky.

Suddenly...

...the inky heavens exploded with huge sparkling stars!
God placed a brilliant fiery ball, the sun, to hang radiant in the sky by day
and a luminous silver moon to light the velvety black sky by night.

And God saw that it was good!

God looked at the marvelous green leaves
and decided to make yellow, orange, and red leaves too—
to live together in His new forest!

A burst of wild wind carried those green, yellow, orange, and red leaves high up into the air where they sailed and danced together, filling the sky with a whirlwind of joyful color.

But that was not all....

Next, God made swimming creatures
to live in the wide blue waters.

God had fun when He made fish!

He made violet fish with indigo stripes
and dashing white fish with black and yellow stripes.

He made golden-yellow fish that shimmered like sunlight,
and white-banded orange fish that glimmered like moonlight.

He made blue and green fish
with orange headbands and fanlike fins
and giant blue whales that made great grey shadows
as they sailed through the deep.

And all the new swimmers began to dart, splash,
and glide about in God's glistening blue ocean.

And God saw that it was good!
So what did God make next?

God made the feathered flyers—

God made birds!

He made clever blue and white birds
and cheerful white and pink birds.

He made black-beaked talking birds
and greenish-yellow chatting birds.

He made silver-grey birds with golden crowns
and lively yellow birds with rosy faces.

He made beige and brown camouflaged birds
and fast-flying red birds that could actually whistle!

When God made butterflies
He used all His colors!

He made brilliant blue butterflies with dazzling wings
and big beige butterflies, spotted and bejeweled.

He made ruby red butterflies in handsome black and white
and stained-glass butterflies in shimmering orange.

He made round yellow butterflies bobbling on the breeze and majestic violet butterflies with lacelike wings.

Together, the color-box of butterflies flitted here and there in the dappled light of the green, yellow, orange, and red forest.

Soon it was sunset....

As the deep purple evening moved through the trees,
a soft, sweet-scented breeze cooled the air.

God's night light, the moon, rose in the heavens
and shone a gentle silver glow over the earth.

The butterflies gathered and settled down to rest
with their blue, black, brown, and beige friends.

Soothing night sounds filled the woodlands
as hidden creatures began to sing their evening songs.

The symphony of creation sang in harmony.
But something was still missing....

As the next day dawned,
God painted golden-amber clouds
in the early morning sky.

It was time to make the animals!

He made sleek orange tigers with long white whiskers
and powerful yellow lions with bushy tawny manes.
He made brown spotted giraffes with necks like tree trunks
and fancy black and white zebras that knew how to gallop.

He even made mysterious, bright-eyed chameleons that could
change the color of their orange, red, green, blue, and white skin!
God made friendly pink-tongued puppy dogs, fluffy blue-eyed
kittens, and every other kind of animal that lives on the earth!

God looked over the expanding world.

The seas rolled.
The clouds swelled.

The breezes blew.
The whales dived.

The birds sang
and the animals moved about
the fresh, flourishing earth.

And God saw that it was good!

But was God finished yet? No, He was not finished yet.

It was time to make His most marvelous creation—His Children!
...And what did God's children look like?

God made some of His children with green eyes
like the great green leaves.

He made some of His children with brown eyes
like the rich brown earth.

He made some of His children with blue eyes
like the wide blue ocean.

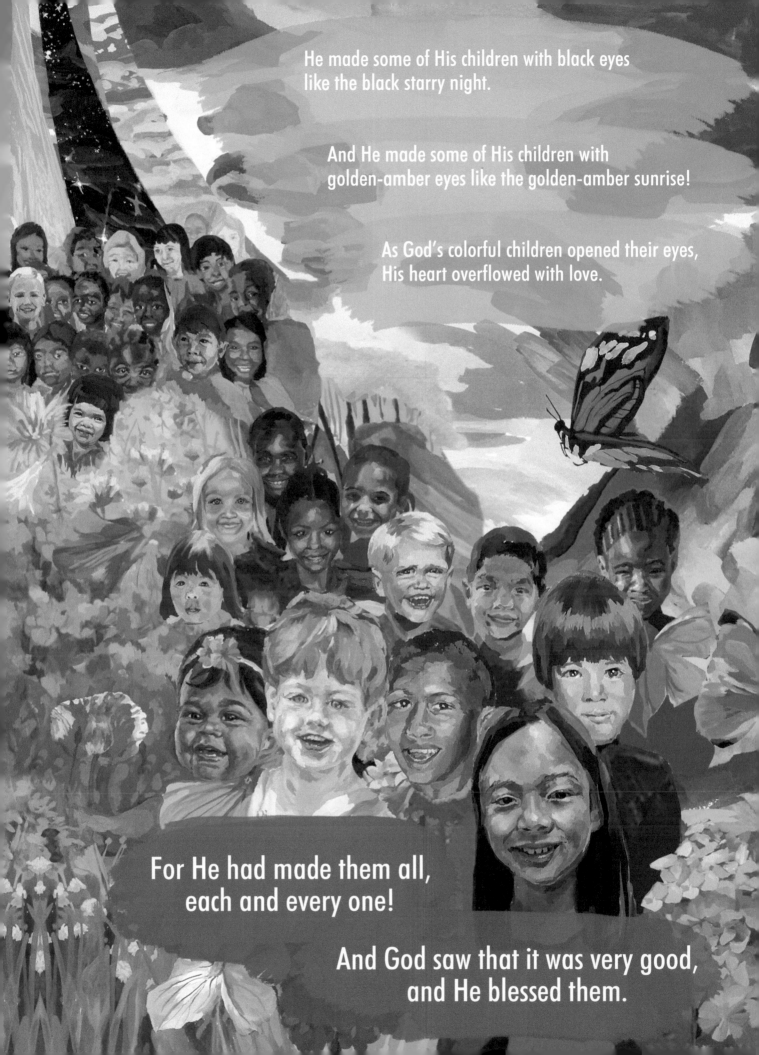

He made some of His children with black eyes
like the black starry night.

And He made some of His children with
golden-amber eyes like the golden-amber sunrise!

As God's colorful children opened their eyes,
His heart overflowed with love.

For He had made them all,
each and every one!

And God saw that it was very good,
and He blessed them.

CPSIA information can be obtained
at www.ICGtesting.com
Printed in the USA
BVHW021718250319
543612BV00004B/45/P